Key Stage 2

Spelling

Carol Matchett

Name _____

Schofield & Sims

Being able to spell words correctly is important because it makes your writing easier to read. If many words are spelt incorrectly it is difficult for the reader to follow what you have written. Being able to spell also helps you as a writer. If you can spell words easily you can spend more time thinking about *what* you are writing.

This book will help you to improve your spelling. It includes basic spelling strategies, common problem areas and useful spelling rules and guidelines.

Finding your way around this book

Before you start using this book, write your name in the name box on the first page.

Then decide how to begin. If you want a complete course on spelling, you should work right through the book from beginning to end. Another way to use the book is to dip into it when you want to find out about a particular topic, such as silent letters. The Contents page will help you to find the pages you need.

Whichever way you choose, don't try to do too much at once – it's better to work through the book in short bursts.

When you have found the topic you want to study, look out for these icons, which mark different parts of the text. **You may find it useful to have a dictionary nearby so that you can check any spellings you are not sure about.**

This icon shows you the activities that you should complete. You write your answers in the spaces provided. After you have worked through all the activities on the page, turn to pages 39 to 48 to check your answers. When you are sure that you understand the topic, put a tick in the box beside it on the Contents page.

On page 38 you will find suggestions for some projects (**Now you try**), which will give you further practice in spelling.

This text explains the topic and gives examples. Make sure you read it before you start the activities.

This text gives you useful background information about the subject.

Contents

Spelling words: the right choice

Explanation

Lots of short words can be spelt by breaking them up into **phonemes** (sounds), and then writing the letters that make those sounds. However, there is often more than one way to spell a sound so you need to choose the right letters for that word.

Example t-**or**-n   w-**ar**-m   b-**oar**-d   f-**our**-th

All these words have the **same vowel sound** but it is **spelt differently** in each word.

Activities

1 Choose the correct spelling for the **vowel sound** to complete these words.

a gr _____ p	**oo** **ou**	**f** s _____ prise	**er** **ur**
b pr _____ d	**ou** **ow**	**g** w _____ ld	**er** **or**
c gr _____ t	**ai** **ea**	**h** c _____ nt	**ou** **ow**
d f _____ ty	**or** **our**	**i** forw _____ d	**er** **ar**
e p _____ pose	**ur** **er**	**j** p _____ haps	**er** **ur**

2 Look at these **compound words**. One part of each word is spelt wrongly. Write each compound word correctly.

a erthworm	_____	**f** grapefroot	_____
b overherd	_____	**g** heartbraik	_____
c evrybody	_____	**h** headquorters	_____
d iyesight	_____	**i** meenwhile	_____
e boyfrend	_____	**j** therfore	_____

Did you know?

The English alphabet has 26 letters, but only five are **vowels** (the letters **a**, **e**, **i**, **o** and **u**). The vowels are used in lots of different combinations to make about 20 different vowel sounds. This is why choosing the right spelling for vowel sounds can be difficult.

Checking your spelling

Explanation

If you want to improve your spelling, **check** everything you write, looking for spelling mistakes.

When you write a word, look at it. Does it **look right**? You will start being a good speller when you can see if a word looks right.

Activities

1 Look closely at the words in these sentences. One word in each sentence is spelt incorrectly. Underline that word. Write it correctly.

a There were far too meny of us in the hall.   _____

b We go back to sckuul next Tuesday.   _____

c Warter was pouring out all over the floor.   _____

d I wud have liked to go but I was too busy.   _____

e In the street, peepel were shouting and cheering.   _____

f Simon offten sees the funny side of things.   _____

2 Tick the correct spelling of these words.

a shure ☐   sure ☐   **g** harf ☐   half ☐

b because ☐   becorse ☐   **h** bizy ☐   busy ☐

c pretty ☐   pritty ☐   **i** young ☐   yung ☐

d byootiful ☐   beautiful ☐   **j** tuch ☐   touch ☐

e prove ☐   proove ☐   **k** towards ☐   towords ☐

f stedy ☐   steady ☐   **l** walk ☐   wark ☐

Syllables

Explanation

Long words are made up of **syllables**. Syllables are like the beats in a word. **Each syllable** has a **vowel**. Breaking words into syllables can help you to spell long words. Say and spell each syllable in turn.

Example af/ter/noon (3 syllables) in/vi/ta/tion (4 syllables) hip/po/po/ta/mus (5 syllables)

Activities

1 Split these words into **syllables**. Draw a line between the syllables. The first one has been done.

a consider → ___con/si/der___   g develop → _____

b remember → _____   h important → _____

c following → _____   i disgusting → _____

d information → _____   j operation → _____

e probably → _____   k experiment → _____

f material → _____   l particular → _____

2 Add the missing syllable in each of these words.

a fan __ __ __ tic   d un __ __ __ stand   g sud __ __ __ ly

b en __ __ __ tain   e di __ __ saur   h Sep __ __ __ ber

c re __ __ __ mend   f frigh __ __ __ ing   i in __ __ __ fere

3 Add the missing letters in these words. Use the clues to help you.

a u __ /b __ __ __ /l __ (something to use when it rains)

b d __ __ /f __ /c __ __ __ (not easy)

c i __ /t __ __ /__ i/g __ __ __ (very clever)

d i __ /m __ /d __ /ate (instant)

Words within words

Explanation

Looking for **smaller words** inside long words can sometimes help you remember how to spell long words.

Example mother → other moth her he the   soldier → sold old die

Activities

1 See if you can find three or four little words inside these longer words.

a vegetable   → _____

b potatoes   → _____

c according   → _____

d programme   → _____

e instrument   → _____

2 Complete these words by adding one of the little words from the box.

tin	toes	late	nut	lie	pet

a be _____ ve   **c** mi _____ e   **e** toma _____

b com _____ ition   **d** con _____ ue   **f** choco _____

3 In each of these words, underline a three- or four-letter word that will help you remember **how to spell** the long word.

a favourite   **d** bargain   **g** money   **j** mathematics

b position   **e** recognise   **h** explanation   **k** learning

c calendar   **f** accident   **i** restaurant   **l** environment

Learning tricky words

Explanation

Many words are **not spelt** exactly **as they sound**.

Example busy   sugar   guide

You just have to **learn to spell** words like these. But in most words it is just a few letters that are not spelt as you would expect. So you can learn to spell these words by looking for the **tricky part** and learning to picture it in the word.

Activities

1 Look closely at each of these words. Underline the **part of each word** that you find **tricky**. Try to picture each word in your head.

guard	peculiar	special	length	bruise	ancient
actual	February	queue	rhyme	awkward	answer

2 Now cover up the words in the box above. Add the missing letters in these words.

g __ __ rd   Feb __ __ __ ry   len __ th   __ __ kw __ __ d

act __ __ l   spe __ __ al   r __ __ me   an __ __ ent

p __ c __ li __ r   que __ __   br __ __ se   ans __ __ r

3 Keep the words in the box covered. Write the correct spelling of each of these words.

a perculier _____   **e** lenth _____

b Febuary _____   **f** awkwerd _____

c ryhme _____   **g** broose _____

d speciul _____   **h** aincent _____

When you have finished activities 2 and 3, check your answers against the correct spellings shown in activity 1.

Using a dictionary

You can use a **dictionary** to help check the **correct spelling** of a word. To find a word in a dictionary you need to have a good idea about the **first few letters**.

Example enthusiasm

Knowing the first four letters helps you find the word 'enthusiasm'.

Activities

1 Use a **dictionary** to find the words beginning with these letters.

a bui __ __ __ __ g

f guar __ __ __ __ e

k nui __ __ __ __ __

b fasc __ __ __ __ __

g veh __ __ __ __

l thor __ __ __ __

c rhy __ __ m

h obed __ __ __ t

m ridi __ __ __ __ __ __

d hau __ __ __ d

i exag __ __ __ __ __ __

n cem __ __ __ __ __

e nau __ __ __ __

j yac __ __

o skel __ __ __ __

2 Underline the **spelling error** in each sentence. Use a dictionary to help you write the correct spelling.

a He came twelth out of forty.   _____

b She spoke a foreign langage.   _____

c I suppose I can't perswade you.   _____

d He played amature football in his youth.   _____

e Tonight is a special occassion.   _____

f We walked through the magnifisent hall.   _____

Some words are difficult to find in a dictionary. For example, you won't find 'rhinoceros' if you look for words starting 'rino'. If you can't find a word, try an alternative spelling.

Tricky word endings

Explanation

Some **word endings** are difficult because they are **not spelt as they sound**. Read aloud the words below. Listen to the endings and look at how they are spelt.

Example fic**tion**   pic**ture**   clo**sure**   jeal**ous**

These four endings are found on lots of words so it is important to recognise them and learn to spell them correctly.

Activities

1 These words all end with a 'shun' sound. Write in the correct spelling.

    a sta _____

    b mo _____

    c tradi _____

    d men _____

    e na _____

    f func _____

    g lo _____

    h sec _____

    i condi _____

    j posi _____

    k frac _____

    l ambi _____

2 Complete these words by adding the ending –ture or –sure.

    a mea _____

    b na _____

    c fu _____

    d crea _____

    e plea _____

    f clo _____

    g trea _____

    h adven _____

    i fea _____

    j furni _____

    k lei _____

    l mix _____

3 Complete these words. Use the clues to help you.

    a en __ __ m __ __ __ (very big)

    b s __ ri __ __ __ (not funny)

    c pr __ vi __ __ __ (the one before)

    d a __ xi __ __ __ (worried)

    e c __ ri __ __ __ (interested)

    f dang __ r __ __ __ (not safe)

    g obvi __ __ __ (clear)

    h fab __ l __ __ __ (wonderful)

    i trem __ __ d __ __ __ (great, incredible)

    j n __ __ v __ __ __ (timid, on edge)

Word endings: –le, –el, –al, –ol

Explanation

Some **word endings** are difficult because they **sound the same** but are **spelt differently**.

Example

candle   **–le** is the most common spelling (it often follows **tall letters** or **descenders**).

parcel   **–el** is less common, but it often follows **c, m, n, r, s, v, w** or **soft g**.

metal   only a few **nouns** end **–al**, but it is often added to root words to form **adjectives**.

pistol   only a few words end **–ol**.

Activities

1   Use the first two guidelines to help you decide whether **–le** or **–el** is needed for each of these words.

a tick __ __	**e** need __ __	**i** tunn __ __	**m** horrib __ __
b canc __ __	**f** stap __ __	**j** bott __ __	**n** simp __ __
c kenn __ __	**g** sett __ __	**k** tramp __ __	**o** trav __ __
d spark __ __	**h** quarr __ __	**l** hand __ __	**p** cam __ __

2   Use the guidelines to help you sort these words into the correct box.

magic __ __   med __ __   ped __ __   person __ __   petr __ __

capit __ __   tradition __ __   tropic __ __   id __ __   anim __ __

Nouns ending –al	–al added to a root word	Nouns ending –ol

Spelling guidelines like this are not straightforward. There are always some words that do not fit the pattern. Look out for unexpected spellings.

Example label   model

Common letter strings

Explanation

Sometimes you see the same **strings of letters** in many words. These letter strings can represent **different sounds** in different words.

Example c**ould**   w**ould**   sh**ould**   sh**ould**er   m**ould**

Look out for words with the same letter string and **learn them as a group** even if the letter string makes a different sound.

Activities

1 Complete these word chains by adding other words with the **same letter string** (even if the sound is different). The first one has been started for you.

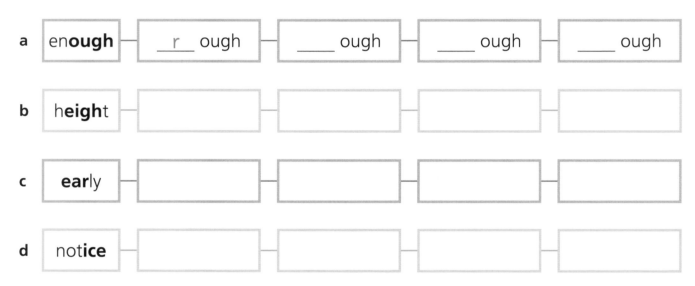

a en**ough** — __r__ ough — ____ ough — ____ ough — ____ ough

b h**eigh**t

c **ear**ly

d not**ice**

2 Look at the words in the box below. Find the pairs of words that have the same letter string but **different sounds**.

quest   drought   caught   flavour   laugh   courage   antique   thought

Write each pair of words below. Think of an extra word for each letter string and add it to the box.

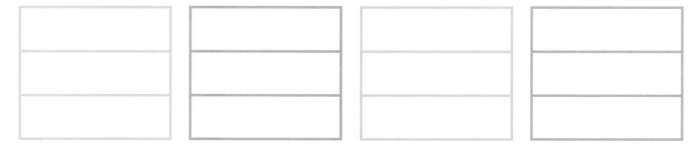

Soft and hard letter sounds

Sometimes the same letter can represent **different sounds** in different words. The letter **c** usually makes a hard **'k'** sound, but in some words **c** is used to make a soft **'s'** sound.

Example **ce**ntury   **ci**ty   **cy**cle

The letter **c** makes an **'s'** sound only **before e, i** or **y**.

Activities

1 Read these words aloud. Underline the **soft c** and the letter that follows it. Check that the words follow the rule.

circle	centre	decide	cyclone	pencil	certain
sincere	cylinder	recent	exercise	accident	Cyprus

The letter **g** usually makes a hard **'g'** sound, but it is often used to make a soft **'j'** sound **before e, i** and **y**.

Example **ge**nius   ma**gic**   ener**gy**

2 Read these words aloud. Underline the **soft g** and the letter that follows it. Check that the words follow the rule.

giant	gentle	strange	gym	suggest	emergency
giraffe	engine	ginger	general	danger	origin

3 Add the missing letters in these words

a re ___ ___ pe   (found in a cookery book)

b ex ___ ___ llent   (very, very good)

c ur ___ ___ nt   (needed immediately)

d ima ___ ___ ne   (to picture in your mind)

Watch out for words that do not follow the **soft g** rule.

Example ma**je**sty   sub**je**ct

Unusual spellings

Explanation

Some words are tricky because a sound is spelt in an **unusual way**.

In some words the **'f'** sound is spelt **ph**.   **Example** dolphin   alphabet   orphan

In some words the **'i'** sound is spelt **y**.   **Example** crystal   lyrics   cynic

Activities

1 Each of these book titles contains **two** spelling errors. Underline the errors and write both words correctly.

a Learn fonics with Emma the elefant   _____   _____

b Miths and legends of Egipt   _____   _____

c A sistem of signs and simbols   _____   _____

d A fisical workout at the gim   _____   _____

e The mistery of the Great Piramid   _____   _____

In some words a **'k'** sound is **spelt ch**.   **Example** orchestra   ache

In other words a **'sh'** sound is **spelt ch**.   **Example** charades   chauffeur

2 Read these words. Write them in the correct box.

| scheme | chorus | chef | chemist | chalet | character |
| stomach | machine | brochure | echo | parachute | sachet |

'k' sound spelt ch	'sh' sound spelt ch

Did you know?

Words with a **'k'** sound spelt **ch** are often Greek in origin (like '**ch**oir', originally used in ancient Greek plays). A **'sh'** sound spelt **ch** is found in words of French origin, (like '**ch**ampagne', named after an area of France).

Silent letters

Activities

1 Read these words aloud. Underline the silent consonant.

a	lamb	**c**	solemn	**e**	island	**g**	gnaw	**i**	knee
b	rhubarb	**d**	fasten	**f**	psalm	**h**	wreckage	**j**	debt

2 Add the silent letter that is missing from each of these sentences.

a The ___night had a ___nack for ___nitting in ___nots.

Silent ___

b Lis___en to the whis___le of the wind through the cas___le.

Silent ___

c I ___rote the ___rong address on the ___rapper.

Silent ___

3 Add the silent letter that is missing from each of these words.

a	___ nock	**e**	s ___ ord	**i**	crum ___
b	colum ___	**f**	___ rinkle	**j**	___ narled
c	___ nife	**g**	bom ___	**k**	ans ___ er
d	this ___ le	**h**	dou ___ t	**l**	autum ___

Did you know?

Hundreds of years ago, silent letters such as **k** in knight would have been pronounced. Over the centuries, the way we say the words has changed but the original spelling has been kept.

–ie or –ei?

Explanation

The letters **i** and **e** are often found together. The problem is knowing whether the spelling is **ie** or **ei**. The rule '**i before e**, **except after c**' is very useful, but you need to know that it only works when the **ie** or **ei** makes a **long ee sound**.

Example thief   shield   (**i** before **e** because there is no **c**)

deceive   (**ei** because it comes after **c**)

If the letters make a **long 'ay'** sound, the spelling is usually **ei**.

Example neighbour   vein   reins

Activities

1 Use the rules above to help you tick the correct spelling of these words.

a achieve ☐   acheive ☐   **f** neice ☐   niece ☐

b mischeif ☐   mischief ☐   **g** ceiling ☐   cieling ☐

c weight ☐   wieght ☐   **h** piece ☐   peice ☐

d believe ☐   beleive ☐   **i** conciet ☐   conceit ☐

e recieve ☐   receive ☐   **j** shriek ☐   shreik ☐

2 Underline the misspelt word in each sentence. Write it correctly.

a The chief was relieved to escape from the fierce battle.   _____

b I believe my decietful neighbour stole the receipt.   _____

c The mischeivous monkey escaped with eight bananas.   _____

There are some exceptions to the **i before e except after c** rule that you need to learn.

Example either   neither   protein   seize   weird

Spelling

Unstressed vowels

Explanation

Some long words are tricky to spell because they have a **vowel** that is **difficult to hear** when you say the word normally. Read these words aloud.

Example Saturday   skeleton

In these words it is difficult to hear one or more vowel sounds in the middle. You can remember the correct spelling by **saying all the syllables** clearly: Sa-**tur**-day   ske-**le**-ton.

Activities

1 Read each of these words aloud normally. Underline any **vowels** that are difficult to hear.

a animal

b factory

c library

d history

e grammar

f popular

g interest

h average

i general

Say these words again in a way that helps you to hear the vowel you have underlined.

2 Add the missing vowels to complete these words.

a sev __ r __ l

b def __ n __ te

c perm __ n __ nt

d priv __ l __ ge

e ord __ n __ ry

f s __ nt __ nce

g desp __ r __ te

h rel __ v __ nt

i cat __ g __ ry

j parli __ m __ nt

k d __ scr __ be

l pr __ j __ dice

m mis __ r __ ble

n temp __ r __ tw

o secr __ t __ ry

3 Tick the correct spelling of each of these words.

a company ☐   compeny ☐

b diffarent ☐   different ☐

c seperate ☐   separate ☐

d similar ☐   similer ☐

Homophones 1

Explanation

Homophones are words that **sound the same**, but are **not spelt the same** and they have completely **different meanings**. The problem with spelling these words is knowing which word is which.

Example stairs (steps up and down) and stares (looks very hard)

isle (an island) and aisle (a gangway)

Activities

1 Read these two lists of words aloud. Join the pairs that **sound the same**.

main	steal
serial	reign
rain	mane
steel	waist
aloud	cereal
waste	allowed

2 Complete these pairs of **homophones**. Use the clues to help you.

a mail and _____ (man or boy)

b heel and _____ (make better)

c peace and _____ (a part of something)

d groan and _____ (when something has become larger)

3 Add the correct homophone in each space so that these sentences make sense. Choose from the words in pink.

a I wonder _____ the _____ will stay fine. **weather whether**

b In the murk and _____, we _____ the turning. **missed mist**

c I can _____ singing coming from in _____. **here hear**

d I _____ it was not my coat. Mine was brand _____. **new knew**

e Who _____ the stone _____ the window? **threw through**

Homophones 2

Explanation

Some words are **not quite homophones** but they still get confused because they look and **sound very similar**.

Example quite and quiet

As with homophones, you need to learn which word is which.

Activities

1 Choose the correct word to complete these sentences.

a Thunder and _____ is scary. **lightening lightning**

b It was a _____ result for us. **dissent decent**

c _____ to the entrance. **Proceed Precede**

d Shall we have ice cream for _____? **desert dessert**

e The long journey made me _____. **wary weary**

2 Choose the **verb** to complete these sentences.

a We must _____ a plan. **device devise**

b Let me _____ you. **advice advise**

c I _____ every day. **practice practise**

d Bad weather _____ us all. **affects effects**

e Please _____ this small gift. **accept except**

3 Write the **noun** that is the homophone or near homphone of these **verbs**.

a led and _____   d passed and _____

b guessed and _____   e bury and _____

c seen and _____   f heard and _____

Did you know?

Some contractions (or shortened forms) also create homophones. For example, he'll and heel, heal; they're and their and there; who's and whose.

Adding –s and –es 1

Explanation

To change a **noun** into a **plural** you usually **add –s** to the end.

Example one book → lots of books   one car → many cars

However, when the **plural ending** sounds like **'is'**, you **add –es**.

Example bus → bus**es**   wish → wish**es**   patch → patch**es**   tax → tax**es**

Notice that the **'is'** sound adds an **extra syllable** or beat to the end of these words.

Activities

1 Write the **plural** of these words in the correct box.

| hundred | brush | hour | guess | switch |
| month | address | sandwich | parent | dozen |

Plural ending –s	Plural ending –es ('is' sound)

Some words that end with **–f** or **–fe** change to **–ves** in the plural form.

Example wol**f** → wol**ves**   loa**f** → loa**ves**   scar**f** → scar**ves**

2 Follow this rule to change these words to plurals.

a one knife → six _____

b one life → nine _____

c one thief → a gang of _____

d one half → two _____

e one leaf → hundreds of _____

f one shelf → two _____

Look out for exceptions to this rule.   **Example** chie**f** → chie**fs**   belie**f** → belie**fs**

Adding –s and –es 2

Explanation

Be careful with words **ending y**. If the word has a **consonant before the y**, then **change y to i** and **add –es**.

Example la**dy** → lad**ies**   pup**py** → pupp**ies**   co**py** → cop**ies**

If there is a **vowel before the y**, just **add –s**.

Example monk**ey** → monkey**s**

Activities

1   Write the **plural** spelling of these words.

a enemy   _____   **f** story   _____

b chimney   _____   **g** dictionary   _____

c opportunity _____   **h** journey   _____

d country   _____   **i** factory   _____

e memory   _____   **j** valley   _____

The spelling rules you have learnt on pages 20–21 are also used to **add –s or –es** to the end of **verbs**.

Example I stretch → he stretch**es**   I worr**y** → she worr**ies**

2   Complete these sentences. Add **–s** or **–es** to the **verbs** in brackets.

a He (finish) _____ packing and (attach) _____ a label.

b Sam (fancy) _____ pizza and Jack (agree) _____ .

c She (copy) _____ the letter and (reply) _____ at once.

d Mum (relax) _____ and (discuss) _____ her day.

e Dad (embarrass) _____ me when he (watch) _____ me play.

f The wand (touch) _____ the frog and it (vanish) _____ .

Adding –ed and –ing 1

Explanation

For most words it is easy to **add –ing** or **–ed** to the end of **verbs**.

Example remain → remain**ed**   remain**ing**

But if the word **ends –e**, then **drop the –e** before adding **–ing** or **–ed**.

Example surprise → surpris**ed**   surpris**ing**

Activities

1 Use the rule to add **–ing** or **–ed** to these words. Write the **–ing** and **–ed** words in the correct column. The first one has been done for you.

invent   arrive   promise   follow   complete   increase
protect   breathe   remain   produce   assist   mutter

Just add –ing and –ed	Drop the –e and add –ing and –ed
inventing invented	

2 Write the correct spelling of the **verb** in these sentences.

a They are always argueing.   _____

b A sudden noise frightend everyone.   _____

c He attractid a lot of attention.   _____

d I was determind to win.   _____

e The floods are damageing the crops.   _____

Adding –ed and –ing 2

If a word ends with a **consonant and y**, then **change y to i** before **adding –ed**, but **not before –ing** (or you would get **ii**).

Example carry + **ed** → carr**ied**   but   carry + **ing** → carr**ying**

Only use this rule if the word ends with a **consonant and y**. If there is a **vowel before the y**, just **add –ed** or **–ing**.

Example obey → obey**ed**   obey**ing**

Activities

1   Use the rule to add **–ed** and **–ing** to these words.

a   bury + ed → _____   + ing → _____

b   rely + ed → _____   + ing → _____

c   reply + ed → _____   + ing → _____

d   study + ed → _____   + ing → _____

e   vary + ed → _____   + ing → _____

f   occupy + ed → _____   + ing → _____

g   annoy + ed → _____   + ing → _____

h   satisfy + ed → _____   + ing → _____

i   supply + ed → _____   + ing → _____

j   accompany + ed → _____   + ing → _____

2   Tick the correct spelling of these words.

a   tried ☐   tryed ☐   d   copyed ☐   copied ☐

b   enjoyd ☐   enjoyed ☐   e   hurryed ☐   hurried ☐

c   emptyed ☐   emptied ☐   f   surveyed ☐   surveyd ☐

Adding –ed and –ing 3

Explanation

If a word ends with a **short vowel sound** before a **single consonant**, then the **final consonant** is usually doubled before adding **–ed** or **–ing**. The double letter helps to keep the vowel sound short.

Example grip + **ed** → gri**pped**   begin + **ing** → begi**nning**

Activities

1   Use the rule above to add **–ed** to these words.

a flop_____   **c** brag_____   **e** marvel_____   **g** admit_____

b expel_____   **d** prefer_____   **f** commit_____   **h** rebel_____

2   Use the rule to add **–ing** to these words.

a split_____   **c** forget_____   **e** upset_____   **g** forbid_____

b swap_____   **d** permit_____   **f** kidnap_____   **h** regret_____

When a **two-syllable word** has an **unstressed syllable**, then the final consonant is usually **not doubled**.

Example glist**en** + **ed** → gliste**ned**

3   Add **–ing** or **–ed** to the verbs in brackets so these sentences make sense.

a They were (whisper) _____ and (gossip) _____ .

b What (happen) _____ when you (visit) _____ Joe?

c (Gallop) _____ hooves (clatter) _____ into the yard.

d He (open) _____ the door and (listen) _____ .

e I have (abandon) _____ (garden) _____ for today.

f A (tower) _____ office block (limit) _____ the view.

Always **double the l** on two-syllable words ending **–l**   **Example** travelled   quarrelled

Adding other endings

The three rules you have learnt on pages 22–24 can be used to add other endings such as **–er**, **–est**, **–en**, **–ish** and **–y** to words.

Example

Drop the e rule	late → lat**er**	lat**est**			
Change y to i rule	early → earl**ier**	earl**iest**			
Double consonant rule	fat → fa**tter**	fa**ttest**	fa**tten**	fa**ttish**	fa**tty**

Activities

1 Use these rules to help you **check** the spelling of these words. Underline the **incorrect** spelling on each line. Write it correctly.

a closer littlest largeish icy liken _____

b sooner cooller gladden snobbish beaten _____

c swimmer shredder flipers stopper kidnapper _____

d uglyest angrier prickliest busiest murkier _____

2 Use the rules to add **–y** to these words to make pairs of **synonyms** (words with the same meaning).

a taste __y__ and yum __my__   **f** spice _____ and pepper _____

b grease _____ and fat _____   **g** scare _____ and creep _____

c breeze _____ and gust _____   **h** jitter _____ and nerve _____

d fog _____ and haze _____   **i** slop _____ and slush _____

e water _____ and run _____   **j** sparkle _____ and shine _____

3 One word in each sentence is spelt incorrectly. Underline that word and write it correctly.

a The gardener had forgoten his watering can.   _____

b The foollish beginner has not listened.   _____

c Travelling on slipery roads can be frightening.   _____

d After the robbery we were forbiden from entering.   _____

Adding prefixes 1

Explanation

A **prefix** is a group of letters that can be **added to the beginning of a word**. A prefix changes the **meaning** of the word, but it does not change the spelling.

Example **un** + kind → unkind   **mis** + behave → misbehave   **re** + visit → revisit

Spelling words like this is easy, as long as you know the prefix.

Activities

1   Complete these word sums. Just add the **prefix** to the beginning of the word.

a   mis + lead = _____

b   pre + view = _____

c   anti + freeze = _____

d   sub + merge = _____

e   al + ready = _____

f   inter + act = _____

g   re + cycle = _____

h   dis + agree = _____

i   un + pleasant = _____

j   de + compose = _____

k   al + together = _____

l   mis + behave = _____

2   Choose the correct prefix to add to each of the words.

mis	anti	re	pre	non	ex	sub	al	dis

a   [   ]   clockwise

b   [   ]   historic

c   [   ]   marine

d   [   ]   though

e   [   ]   sense

f   [   ]   honest

g   [   ]   build

h   [   ]   fortune

i   [   ]   change

Did you know?

Many of these prefixes come from ancient languages. For example, **anti** (Greek, meaning 'against'), **sub** (Latin, meaning 'under') and **inter** (Latin, meaning 'between').

Adding prefixes 2

The **spelling** of the prefix and the root word **always stays the same**, even if the prefix ends with the same letter as the word starts.

Example **im** + **m**ature → i**mm**ature   **mis** + **s**pell → mi**ss**pell

This explains why there is a **double letter** in these words.

Activities

1 Complete these pairs of **opposites** by using these **prefixes**. You can use a prefix more than once.

dis	un	in	im	ir	il

a visible and _____

b appear and _____

c conscious and _____

d responsible and _____

e patient and _____

f mortal and _____

g experienced and _____

h possible and _____

i legal and _____

j obey and _____

k usual and _____

l convenient and _____

m legible and _____

n resistible and _____

2 Tick the correct spelling of these words. Think about the word and the prefix to help you decide if there should be a **double letter**.

a irregular ☐
     iregular ☐

b unatural ☐
     unnatural ☐

c interupt ☐
     interrupt ☐

d unecessary ☐
     unnecessary ☐

e inhuman ☐
     innhuman ☐

f disappoint ☐
     dissappoint ☐

g disolve ☐
     dissolve ☐

h immovable ☐
     imovable ☐

i suround ☐
     surround ☐

Adding suffixes

Explanation

A **suffix** is a group of letters that can be **added to the end of a word**. Understanding suffixes can help you to spell lots of words.

Example care + **ful** → careful   music + **al** → musical   wash + **able** → washable

Sometimes **two suffixes** are added to the end of a word.

Example care + **ful** + **ly** → carefully   care + **ful** + **ness** → carefulness

Activities

1 Complete these **suffix** word sums.

a equip + ment = _____

b reason + able = _____

c invent + ive = _____

d final + ly = _____

e wonder + ful + ly = _____

f champion + ship = _____

g breath + less = _____

h plain + ness = _____

i hero + ic = _____

j success + ful = _____

k person + al = _____

l straight + en = _____

2 List 20 words you can make from these root words and suffixes.

Root words:	enjoy	friend	false	hope	rest	king	hard	father
Suffixes:	ment	less	ly	ness	hood	dom	able	ful	ship

_____   _____   _____   _____

_____   _____   _____   _____

_____   _____   _____   _____

_____   _____   _____   _____

_____   _____   _____   _____

Adding suffixes: words ending –e

Explanation

Use these special rules when you add suffixes to words **ending –e**.

If the **suffix begins with a vowel** (a, e, i, o, u), you usually **drop the –e** before adding the suffix. It is called a **vowel suffix**. (For this rule, the **suffix y** also counts as a vowel suffix.)

Example natur**e** + **al** → natural   fam**e** + **ous** → famous   laz**e** + **y** → lazy

If the **suffix begins with a consonant**, you **keep the –e** and add the suffix.

Example lov**e** + **ly** → lovely   advertis**e** + **ment** → advertisement

Activities

1 Use the rule to add these **suffixes** to the root words. The first one has been done.

a strange
- er = stranger
- ness = strangeness

f use
- er =
- ful =

b extreme
- ist =
- ly =

g sure
- est =
- ly =

c forgive
- able =
- ness =

h pure
- ify =
- ness =

d excite
- able =
- ment =

i noise
- y =
- less =

e achieve
- ment =
- able =

j scarce
- ly =
- ity =

Did you know?

There are always some words that do not follow the rules. For example, **argue** ends **–e** but drops the **–e** when for a consonant suffix: argu**e** + **ment** → argument.

Adding suffixes: words ending –y

There is one rule for **adding a suffix** to a word ending with a **consonant** and **y**.
The rule is **change y to i** before adding the suffix.

Example hap**py** → happ**iness**   happ**ily**   happ**ier**   happ**iest**

Use this rule with both **vowel** and **consonant suffixes**.

Activities

1 Use the rule described above to complete these **suffix** word sums.

a   rely + able = _____

b   heavy + ness = _____

c   pity + ful = _____

d   empty + ness = _____

e   merry + ment = _____

f   apology + ise = _____

g   ready + ly = _____

h   destroy + able = _____

i   vary + ous = _____

j   carry + er = _____

k   penny + less = _____

l   plenty + ful = _____

2 Complete this table. Add the three suffixes to the root words.

Root word	Add –est	Add –ly	Add –ness
easy			
naughty			
clumsy			
steady			
lazy			
angry			

Exceptions to suffix rules: –ly and –ous

Activities

1   Use the **main suffix rules** and the **two exceptions** above to add **–ly** to these words.

a false	_____	**e** comic	_____	**i** simple	_____
b humble	_____	**f** immediate	_____	**j** miserable	_____
c basic	_____	**g** frantic	_____	**k** sincere	_____
d gentle	_____	**h** probable	_____	**l** sparkle	_____

2   Use the main suffix rules and the two exceptions to complete these word sums.

a   glamour + ous = _____   **e**   vigour + ous = _____

b   mystery + ous = _____   **f**   courage + ous = _____

c   humour + ous = _____   **g**   glory + ous = _____

d   victory + ous = _____   **h**   fury + ous = _____

Word structure

Explanation

Many long words are made up of a **root word** with a **prefix** or **suffix**. Looking at the **structure** of a word is a good way of spelling longer words.

Example disgracefully = dis   grace   ful ly

                      prefix   root word   suffixes

It can seem much easier to spell a word when you break it up like this.

Activities

1 Cross off any **prefixes** or **suffixes** and find the **root word** in these long words.

a imperfection   _perfect_   **f** unprofessional   _____

b unoriginal   _____   **g** refreshment   _____

c impolitely   _____   **h** secretively   _____

d inexperienced   _____   **i** attractiveness   _____

e dissatisfaction   _____   **j** unfortunately   _____

2 Write a word sum to show how these words are made up of a root word and suffixes.

a supposedly =   _____ + _____ + _____

b loveliness =   _____ + _____ + _____

c effectively =   _____ + _____ + _____

d forgetfulness =   _____ + _____ + _____

e strengthening =   _____ + _____ + _____

f eventually =   _____ + _____ + _____

g reliably =   _____ + _____ + _____

Word families

Explanation

Understanding how words are **related** can help to spell words. **Root words** and other words from the same **word family** often give clues to the correct spelling

Example business = bus**y** + ness (using the **y to i** rule)

Activities

1 Write the **root word** that can help you to spell these longer words. The first one has been done for you.

a government _____govern_____

g knowledge _____

b bicycle _____

h marvellous _____

c criticise _____

i pressure _____

d correspond _____

j especially _____

e opposite _____

k conscience _____

f sufficient _____

l committee _____

2 Join together the **pairs** of words that belong to the same **word family**.

question	various
medicine	muscular
divide	request
muscle	medical
variety	individual
family	design
signature	familiar

Did you know?

The words 'conscience' and 'conscious' are both related to the word 'science'. They all come from the Latin word 'scio', meaning 'I know'.

Word endings: –tion, –sion, –ssion, –cian

Explanation

Lots of words end **–tion** ('shun'). This suffix is often added to a verb to make it into a noun.

Example direct → direc**tion**   complete → comple**tion**

Sometimes the **–tion** ending has a different spelling. The clue comes from the **last letter(s)** of the **root word**.

Example

discu**ss** → discu**ssion**   admi**t** → admi**ssion**   (root words ending **–ss**, **–mit** → **ssion**)

ten**se** → ten**sion**   explo**de** → explo**sion**   (root words ending **–d**, **–de**, **–se** → **sion**)

magi**c** → magi**cian**   (root words ending **c** → **cian**)

Activities

1 Follow the guidelines above to sort these words into the correct box and then write the noun using the correct ending. The first one has been done for you.

~~correct~~	protect	revise	possess	permit	divide
subtract	express	attract	confess	confuse	inspect
impress	invent	decide	precise	expand	extend

–tion	–ssion	–sion
correction		

2 Write the jobs or professions made from these root words.

a music _____

b politic _____

c electric _____

d mathematic _____

e optic _____

f physic _____

Word endings: –able, –ible

Explanation

The **–able** and **–ible** endings cause confusion because they **sound similar**. A good clue is to think about the word without the ending. If there is a **complete root word,** then the spelling is most likely to be **–able**. More words end **–able** than **–ible**.

Example reason**able**   laugh**able**

If there is **no complete root word**, the spelling might well be **–ible**.

Example poss**ible**   vis**ible**

There are some exceptions to this guideline.

Example sens**ible**   forc**ible**   revers**ible**

Activities

1   Use the guidelines above to add **–able** or **–ible** to these words.

a comfort _____

b horr _____

c drink _____

d incred _____

e consider _____

f avail _____

g ed _____

h agree _____

i depend _____

j plaus _____

k enjoy _____

l break _____

m fashion _____

n terr _____

o understand _____

Many words **drop their final –e** when adding **–able**. However, when **–able** is added to words ending **–ce** or **–ge**, the **e is kept**.

Example chang**e** + able = chang**e**able

Some words can **keep or drop the –e** when adding **–able**.

Example likable or likeable   movable or moveable

---

2   Tick the correct spelling of these words.

a adoreable ☐
    adorable ☐

b regrettable ☐
    regretable ☐

c forgiveable ☐
    forgivable ☐

d manageable ☐
    managable ☐

e valuable ☐
    valueable ☐

f noticable ☐
    noticeable ☐

Word endings: –tious, –cious, –tial, –cial

Explanation

There are other word endings that **sound the same** but are **spelt differently**.

Example gra**cious** and cau**tious**   so**cial** and par**tial**

When endings sound the same but are spelt differently, a **root word** or **family word** sometimes gives a clue to the correct spelling (but not always).

Example gra**cious** (gra**ce**)   cau**tious** (cau**tion**)   so**cial** (so**ci**ety)   par**tial** (par**t**)

Activities

1 Complete these adjectives adding **–cious** or **–tious**. Use the clues in brackets to help you. It sometimes includes a helpful **family word** – but not always.

a spa _____ (lots of space)

b deli _____ (very tasty)

c cau _____ (shows caution)

d susp _____ (suspecting)

e nutr _____ (full of nutrition)

f pre _____ (valuable)

g amb _____ (has ambition)

h fer _____ (very fierce)

i mal _____ (with malice)

j inf _____ (can infect)

k vic _____ (nasty, savage)

l cons _____ (awake, alert)

The **–cial** ending is more common after a **vowel**.   **Example** so–**cial**
The **–tial** ending is more common after a consonant.   **Example** par–**tial**
However, there are some exceptions.   **Example** ini–**tial**

---

2 Add **–cial** or **–tial** to complete the words in these sentences.

a It is the offi _____ opening of the mar _____ arts centre.

b Torren _____ rain fell on the artifi _____ grass.

c There was a cru _____ error in the confiden _____ file.

d There is a substan _____ finan _____ reward.

e It is essen _____ to deal with poten _____ problems.

Unstressed endings

Explanation

Many **word endings** are **unstressed** when we say them normally. This means it is **difficult to hear** the **vowel sound**. This weak vowel is called the **schwa sound**.

Example expect**a**nt   urg**e**nt   exist**e**nce   hindr**a**nce

Sometimes a **related** word can help, but often you just need to **learn the correct spelling**. **Say the words** with the ending **stressed** to help you remember.

Example ur**gent**   hin**drance**

Activities

1 In each of these sentences all the words are missing the **same** ending: **–ant** or **–ent**. Add the correct ending in each sentence.

a My observ _____ assist _____ was a brilli _____ contest _____ .

b He is confid _____ , independ _____ and an excell _____ stud _____ .

c Avoid frequ _____ accid _____ s or viol _____ incid _____ s.

d It is import _____ that contest _____ s are pleas _____ and toler _____ .

e It is appar _____ she has the tal _____ to be a dec _____ presid _____ .

f The reluct _____ entr _____ was hesit _____ , not ignor _____ .

Words from the same **word family** share the **same spelling pattern**, so once you learn one word you can spell others.

Example hesit**a**te ➞ hesit**a**nt   hesit**a**nce   hesit**a**ncy

2 Use these **family words** to help you spell the related **nouns**.

Family word	Noun –ance or –ence
elegant	
instant	
innocent	
substantial	
obedient	

Family word	Noun –ancy or –ency
infant	
urgent	
truant	
expectant	
decent	

Fun and games

Playing word games like Scrabble, Countdown, Boggle or Hangman can help you improve your spelling. In all these games you need to think about the letters that make up words. While you are practising, it is a good idea to use a dictionary to check the correct spelling of words.

Spelling detective

Be a spelling detective and look for clues on how to spell words. Use your spelling detective skills when learning words in different subjects. For example, in maths find clues to help spell the word 'circumference'.

Example it starts like 'circle', it has four syllables: cir-cum-**fer**-ence.

Sticky note spelling

If you have spellings to learn, try writing each word on a sticky note. Look at each word in turn and underline the tricky part. Get a good picture of the word in your head. Then put the sticky note under the table and try writing the word. Check whether you were right. Place the sticky notes round your room to keep reminding you what the words look like.

Beat the spell check

Try turning off the spell check when using a computer. See if you can spot and correct your own mistakes first. Then switch on the spell check to do a double check. (Always make sure you select UK English when using a spell check.)

Spelling bee

Organise a spelling bee competition for your friends. Write a list of words for everyone to learn to spell. Include some challenging ones! Give everyone a copy of the list so they can practise. Then hold a contest to see who the champion speller is.

Spelling journal

Keep a notebook to record words you want to learn to spell, especially words that you keep getting wrong. Carefully copy the correct spelling into your spelling journal. Then keep checking you spell the word correctly until it sticks and you can remember it.

Answers

Page 4: Spelling words: the right choice

1
a gr**ou**p
b pr**ou**d
c gr**ea**t
d f**or**ty
e p**ur**pose

f s**ur**prise
g w**or**ld
h c**ou**nt
i forw**ar**d
j p**er**haps

2
a **earth**worm
b over**heard**
c **every**body
d **eye**sight
e boy**friend**

f grape**fruit**
g heart**break**
h head**quarters**
i **mean**while
j **there**fore

Page 5: Checking your spelling

1
a There were far too **meny** of us in the hall. many
b We go back to **sckuul** next Tuesday. school
c **Warter** was pouring out all over the floor. water
d I **wud** have liked to go but I was too busy. would
e In the street, **peepel** were shouting and cheering. people
f Simon **offten** sees the funny side of things. often

2
a sure
b because
c pretty
d beautiful
e prove
f steady

g half
h busy
i young
j touch
k towards
l walk

Page 6: Syllables

1
a con/si/der
b re/mem/ber
c fol/low/ing
d in/for/ma/tion
e pro/ba/bly
f ma/te/ri/al

g de/ve/lop
h im/por/tant
i dis/gus/ting
j o/per/a/tion
k ex/pe/ri/ment
l par/ti/cu/lar

2
a fan/**tas**/tic
b en/**ter**/tain
c re/**com**/mend

d un/**der**/stand
e di/**no**/saur
f frigh/**ten**/ing

g sud/**den**/ly
h Sep/**tem**/ber
i in/**ter**/fere

3
a um/brel/la

b dif/fi/cult

c in/tel/li/gent

d im/me/di/ate

Page 7: Words within words

1
a vegetable → get a table tab able
b potatoes → pot at toes a to tat
c according → cord or din ding
d programme → program me ram am
e instrument → in strum men rum

2
a be**lie**ve
b com**pet**ition
c mi**nut**e
d con**tinu**e
e toma**toes**
f choco**late**

3
a fav**our**ite/favou**rite**
b pos**it**ion
c ca**lend**ar
d bar**gain**
e re**cog**nise
f acc**ident**/acci**den**t
g mo**ne**y
h ex**plan**ation
i **rest**a**ur**ant
j ma**the**matics/ma**the**matics
k **learn**ing/lea**rn**ing
l env**iron**ment/environ**men**t

Page 8: Learning tricky words

Check your answers by looking at the correct spellings in the box at the top of the page.

Page 9: Using a dictionary

1
a building
b fascinate
c rhythm
d haunted
e naughty
f guarantee
g vehicle
h obedient
i exaggerate
j yacht
k nuisance
l thorough
m ridiculous
n cemetery
o skeleton

2
a twelfth
b language
c persuade
d amateur
e occasion
f magnificent

Page 10: Tricky word endings

1
a station
b motion
c tradition
d mention
e nation
f function
g lotion
h section
i condition
j position
k fraction
l ambition

2
a mea**s**ure
b nature
c fu**t**ure
d creature
e plea**s**ure
f clo**s**ure
g trea**s**ure
h adven**t**ure
i feature
j furniture
k lei**s**ure
l mixture

3
a enormous
b serious
c previous
d anxious
e curious
f dangerous
g obvious
h fabulous
i tremendous
j nervous

Page 11: Word endings: –le, –el, –al, –ol

1

a tick**le**	**e** need**le**	**i** tunn**el**	**m** horrib**le**
b canc**el**	**f** stap**le**	**j** bott**le**	**n** simp**le**
c kenn**el**	**g** sett**le**	**k** tramp**le**	**o** trav**el**
d spark**le**	**h** quarr**el**	**l** hand**le**	**p** cam**el**

2

Nouns ending –al	–al added to a root word	Nouns ending –ol
medal	magical	petrol
pedal	personal	idol
capital	traditional	
animal	tropical	

Page 12: Common letter strings

1 Here are some examples of words that you may have included in your word chains.

a en**ough**   though although through thorough rough tough cough
b h**eigh**t   weigh weight eight eighth eighty neigh neighbour
c **ear**ly   earth heard heart learn wearing weary appear pear dreary
d not**ice**   price spice practice police justice sacrifice prejudice

2 Here are the pairs of words and some other words you may have included in each box.

quest anti**que**   queue mosque quench queen squeak banquet unique
dr**ought** th**ought**   brought ought bought sought
flav**our** c**our**age   favourite hour your colour tour neighbour honour journal
c**augh**t l**augh**   naughty daughter taught draught

Page 13: Soft and hard letter sounds

1

circle	**ce**ntre	de**ci**de	**cy**clone	pen**ci**l	**ce**rtain
sin**ce**re	**cy**linder	re**ce**nt	exer**ci**se	ac**ci**dent	**Cy**prus

2

giant	**ge**ntle	stran**ge**	**gy**m	sug**ge**st	emer**ge**ncy
giraffe	en**gi**ne	**gi**nger	**ge**neral	dan**ge**r	ori**gi**n

3 **a** re**ci**pe   **b** ex**ce**llent   **c** ur**ge**nt   **d** ima**gi**ne

Page 14: Unusual spellings

1
a Learn **fonics** with Emma the **elefant**   phonics   elephant
b **Miths** and legends of **Egipt**   myths   Egypt
c A **sistem** of signs and **simbols**   system   symbols
d A **fisical** workout at the **gim**   physical   gym
e The **mistery** of the Great **Piramid**   mystery   Pyramid

Answers continued

'k' sound spelt ch	'sh' sound spelt ch
scheme chorus chemist character stomach echo ache	chef chalet machine brochure parachute

Page 15: Silent letters

1 a lamb   c solemn   e island   g gnaw   i knee
b rhubarb   d fasten   f psalm   h wreckage   j debt

2 a knight   knack   knitting   knots   Silent k
b Listen   whistle   castle   Silent t
c wrote   wrong   wrapper   Silent w

3 a knock   e sword   i crumb
b column   f wrinkle   j gnarled
c knife   g bomb   k answer
d thistle   h doubt   l autumn

Page 16: –ie or –ei?

1 a achieve   d believe   g ceiling   j shriek
b mischief   e receive   h piece
c weight   f niece   i conceit

2 a The chief was **relieved** to escape from the fierce battle.   relieved
b I believe my **decietful** neighbour stole the receipt.   deceitful
c The **mischeivous** monkey escaped with eight bananas.   mischievous

Page 17: Unstressed vowels

1 a animal   d history   g interest
b factory   e grammar   h average
c library   f popular   i general

2 a several   f sentence   k describe
b definite   g desperate   l prejudice
c permanent   h relevant   m miserable
d privilege   i category   n temperature
e ordinary   j parliament   o secretary

3 a company   b different   c separate   d similar

Page 18: Homophones 1

1

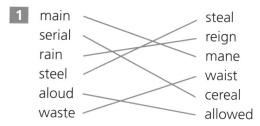

main — mane
serial — cereal
rain — reign
steel — steal
aloud — allowed
waste — waist

2 **a** male **b** heal **c** piece **d** grown

3 **a** I wonder **whether** the **weather** will stay fine.
b In the murk and **mist**, we **missed** the turning.
c I can **hear** singing coming from in **here**.
d I **knew** it was not my coat. Mine was brand **new**.
e Who **threw** the stone **through** the window?

Page 19: Homophones 2

1 **a** Thunder and **lightning** is scary.
b It was a **decent** result for us.
c **Proceed** to the entrance.
d Shall we have ice cream for **dessert**?
e The long journey made me **weary**.

2 **a** We must **devise** a plan.
b Let me **advise** you.
c I **practise** every day.
d Bad weather **affects** us all.
e Please **accept** this small gift.

3 **a** lead **b** guest **c** scene **d** past **e** berry **f** herd

Page 20: Adding –s and –es 1

1

Plural ending –s	Plural ending –es ('is' sound)
hundreds	addresses
parents	guesses
dozens	sandwiches
months	switches
hours	brushes

2 **a** one knife → six knives
b one life → nine lives
c one thief → a gang of thieves
d one half → two halves
e one leaf → hundreds of leaves
f one shelf → two shelves

Page 21: Adding –s and –es 2

1 a enem**ies**   f stor**ies**
  b chimn**eys**   g dictionar**ies**
  c opportunit**ies**   h journ**eys**
  d countr**ies**   i factor**ies**
  e memor**ies**   j vall**eys**

2 a He **finishes** packing and **attaches** a label.
  b Sam **fancies** pizza and Jack **agrees**.
  c She **copies** the letter and **replies** at once.
  d Mum **relaxes** and **discusses** her day.
  e Dad **embarrasses** me when he **watches** me play.
  f The wand **touches** the frog and it **vanishes**.

Page 22: Adding –ed and –ing 1

1

Just add –ing and –ed	Drop the –e and add –ing and –ed
inventing invented	increasing increased
following followed	arriving arrived
protecting protected	promising promised
remaining remained	breathing breathed
assisting assisted	producing produced
muttering muttered	completing completed

2 a arguing   b frightened   c attracted   d determined   e damaging

Page 23: Adding –ed and –ing 2

1 a bury → buried   burying   f occupy → occupied   occupying
  b rely → relied   relying   g annoy → annoyed   annoying
  c reply → replied   replying   h satisfy → satisfied   satisfying
  d study → studied   studying   i supply → supplied   supplying
  e vary → varied   varying   j accompany → accompanied   accompanying

2 a tr**ied**   d cop**ied**
  b enjo**yed**   e hurr**ied**
  c empt**ied**   f surve**yed**

Page 24: Adding –ed and –ing 3

1 a flop**ped**   c brag**ged**   e marvel**led**   g admit**ted**
  b expel**led**   d prefer**red**   f commit**ted**   h rebel**led**

2   **a** splii**ting**   **c** forgett**ing**   **e** upsett**ing**   **g** forbid**ding**
     b swap**ping**   **d** permit**ting**   **f** kidnap**ping**   **h** regrett**ing**

3   **a** They were **whispering** and **gossiping**.
     b What **happened** when you **visited** Joe?
     c **Galloping** hooves **clattered** into the yard.
     d He **opened** the door and **listened**.
     e I have **abandoned gardening** for today.
     f A **towering** office block **limited** the view.

Page 25: Adding other endings

1   **a** lar**g**ish   **b** cooler   **c** fli**pp**ers   **d** ugli**est**

2   **a** tast**y**   yum**my**   **f** spic**y**   pepper**y**
     b greas**y**   fat**ty**   **g** scar**y**   creep**y**
     c breez**y**   gust**y**   **h** jitter**y**   nerv**y**
     d fog**gy**   haz**y**   **i** slo**pp**y   slush**y**
     e water**y**   run**ny**   **j** sparkl**y**   shin**y**

3   **a** forgo**tt**en   **b** foo**l**ish   **c** sli**pp**ery   **d** forbi**dd**en

Page 26: Adding prefixes 1

1   **a** mislead   **g** recycle
     b preview   **h** disagree
     c antifreeze   **i** unpleasant
     d submerge   **j** decompose
     e already   **k** altogether
     f interact   **l** misbehave

2   **a** **anti**clockwise   **d** **al**though   **g** **re**build
     b **pre**historic   **e** **non**sense   **h** **mis**fortune
     c **sub**marine   **f** **dis**honest   **i** **ex**change

Page 27: Adding prefixes 2

1   **a** **in**visible   **h** **im**possible
     b **dis**appear   **i** **il**legal
     c **un**conscious   **j** **dis**obey
     d **ir**responsible   **k** **un**usual
     e **im**patient   **l** **in**convenient
     f **im**mortal   **m** **il**legible
     g **in**experienced   **n** **ir**resistible

2   **a** **ir**regular   **d** **un**necessary   **g** **dis**solve
     b **un**natural   **e** **in**human   **h** **im**movable
     c **inter**rupt   **f** **dis**appoint   **i** **sur**round

Page 28: Adding suffixes

1

a equipment	**g** breathless
b reasonable	**h** plainness
c inventive	**i** heroic
d finally	**j** successful
e wonderfully	**k** personal
f championship	**l** straighten

2 Any 20 words from this list, or variations using two suffixes.

enjoyable	fatherless	hardship	kingly
enjoyment	fatherly	hardness	kingdom
falsehood	friendless	hopeful	kingship
falsely	friendly	hopefully	restful
falseness	friendship	hopeless	restless
fatherhood	hardly	hopelessly	

Page 29: Adding suffixes: words ending –e

1

a stranger strangeness	**f** user useful
b extremist extremely	**g** surest surely
c forgivable forgiveness	**h** purify pureness
d excitable excitement	**i** noisy noiseless
e achievement achievable	**j** scarcely scarcity

Page 30: Adding suffixes: words ending –y

1

a reliable	**d** emptiness	**g** readily	**j** carrier
b heaviness	**e** merriment	**h** destroyable	**k** penniless
c pitiful	**f** apologise	**i** various	**l** plentiful

2

Add –est	**Add –ly**	**Add –ness**
easiest	easily	easiness
naughtiest	naughtily	naughtiness
clumsiest	clumsily	clumsiness
steadiest	steadily	steadiness
laziest	lazily	laziness
angriest	angrily	angriness

Page 31: Exceptions to suffix rules: –ly and –ous

1

a falsely	**d** gently	**g** frantically	**j** miserably
b humbly	**e** comically	**h** probably	**k** sincerely
c basically	**f** immediately	**i** simply	**l** sparkly

2   **a** glamorous   **e** vigorous
    b mysterious   **f** courageous
    c humorous   **g** glorious
    d victorious   **h** furious

Page 32: Word structure

1   **a** perfect   **f** profession
    b origin   **g** fresh
    c polite   **h** secret
    d experience   **i** attract
    e satisfy   **j** fortune

2   **a** suppose + ed + ly   **e** strength + en + ing
    b love + ly + ness   **f** event + (u)al + ly
    c effect + ive + ly   **g** rely + able + ly
    d forget + ful + ness

Page 33: Word families

1   **a** govern   **g** know
    b cycle   **h** marvel
    c critic   **i** press
    d respond   **j** special
    e oppose   **k** science
    f suffice   **l** commit

2

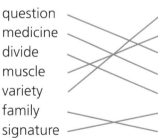

question	various
medicine	muscular
divide	request
muscle	medical
variety	individual
family	design
signature	familiar

Page 34: Word endings: –tion, –sion, –ssion, –cian

1

–tion	–ssion	–sion
correction	possession	revision
protection	expression	division
subtraction	impression	confusion
attraction	permission	decision
inspection	confession	expansion
invention		precision
		extension

2 **a** musician **c** electrician **e** optician
b politician **d** mathematician **f** physician

Page 35: Word endings: –able, –ible

1 **a** comfort**able** **f** avail**able** **k** enjoy**able**
b horr**ible** **g** ed**ible** **l** break**able**
c drink**able** **h** agree**able** **m** fashion**able**
d incred**ible** **i** depend**able** **n** terr**ible**
e consider**able** **j** plaus**ible** **o** understand**able**

2 **a** adorable **c** forgivable **e** valuable
b regrettable **d** manageable **f** noticeable

Page 36: Word endings: –tious, –cious, –tial, –cial

1 **a** spa**c**ious **g** ambi**t**ious
b deli**c**ious **h** fero**c**ious
c cau**t**ious **i** mali**c**ious
d suspi**c**ious **j** infe**ct**ious
e nutri**t**ious **k** vi**c**ious
f pre**c**ious **l** cons**c**ious

2 **a** It is the **official** opening of the **martial** arts centre.
b **Torrential** rain fell on the **artificial** grass.
c There was a **crucial** error in the **confidential** file.
d There is a **substantial financial** reward.
e It is **essential** to deal with **potential** problems.

Page 37: Unstressed endings

1 **a** My observ**ant** assist**ant** was a brilli**ant** contest**ant**.
b He is confid**ent**, independ**ent** and an excell**ent** stud**ent**.
c Avoid frequ**ent** accid**ent**s or viol**ent** incid**ent**s.
d It is import**ant** that contest**ant**s are pleas**ant** and toler**ant**.
e It is appar**ent** she has the tal**ent** to be a dec**ent** presid**ent**.
f The reluct**ant** entr**ant** was hesit**ant**, not ignor**ant**.

2

Family word	Noun –ance or –ence
elegant	eleg**a**nce
instant	inst**a**nce
innocent	innoc**e**nce
substantial	subst**a**nce
obedient	obedi**e**nce

Family word	Noun –ancy or –ency
infant	inf**a**ncy
urgent	urg**e**ncy
truant	tru**a**ncy
expectant	expect**a**ncy
decent	dec**e**ncy